D1283312

We Are Painting

Written by Francie Alexander
Illustrated by Michael Grejniec

Scholastic Inc.
New York   Toronto   London   Auckland   Sydney
Mexico City   New Delhi   Hong Kong

ISBN 0-439-13987-2

1 10 9 8   5/0
                                                                                                                                        62
Printed in China

First Scholastic clubs printing, November 1999

We are painting **green** grass.

We are painting 5 **red** flowers.

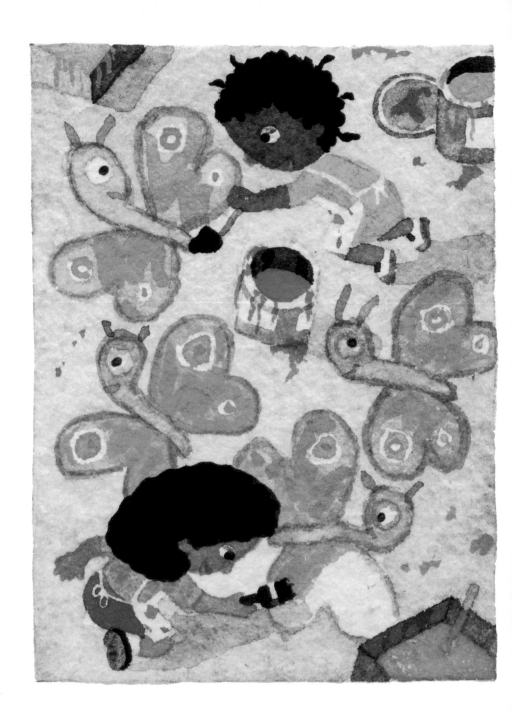

We are painting 4 orange butterflies

We are painting 3 **blue** birds.

We are painting 2 **black** horses.

We are painting 1 yellow sun.

We are painting!